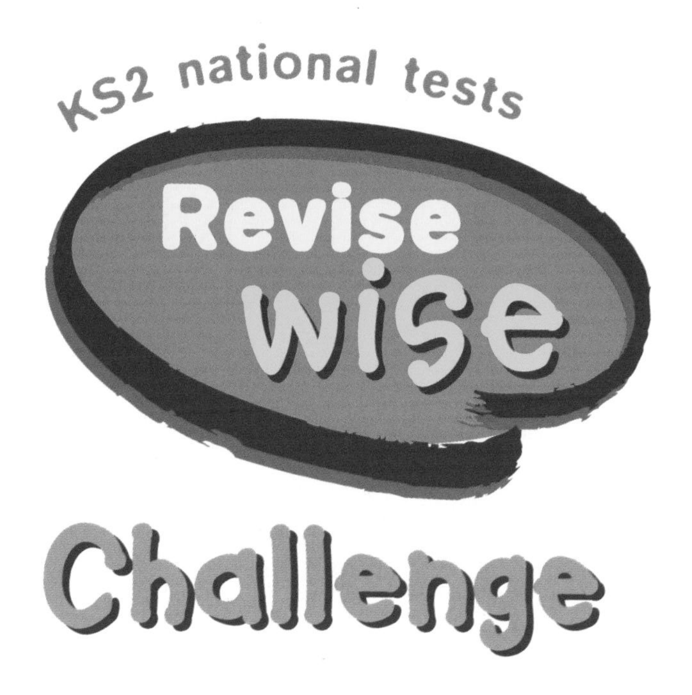

English quiz book

Wendy Wren

ISBN: 0 563 54218 7

Published by BBC Educational Publishing

First published 2000

Designed by Traffika Publishing Ltd.

Illustrated by Julian Baker and Janet Baker

Reproduced by Spectrum Colour, England

Printed in Italy by Poligrafico Dehoniano

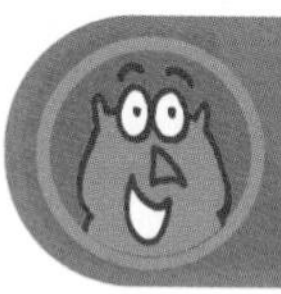

Contents

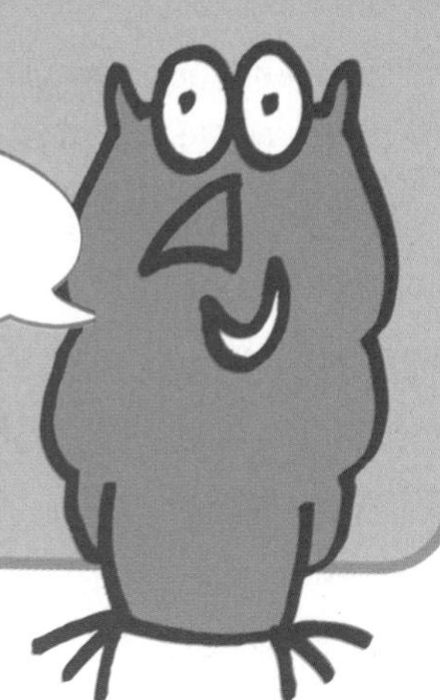

Are you ready for a challenge?

Introduction

What is Key Stage 2 ReviseWise?

In May, Year 6 pupils take their Key Stage 2 (KS2) National Tests In English, Maths and Science. The Tests show teachers what level children are working at. This book is part of the BBC's Key Stage 2 ReviseWise service, created to help children get ready to do their best in all their KS2 National Tests.

The KS2 ReviseWise English resources are:

- this ReviseWise Challenge quiz book
- the ReviseWise English preparation and practice book
- television programmes that you can video
- videos to buy
- a CD-ROM
- a website http://www.bbc.co.uk.revision

There's such a variety of things to do in the whole of ReviseWise that revising need never be boring.

There are even ReviseWise resources for schools, so there's a link between home and school learning.

The ReviseWise English resources have been developed and written by specialists to help children aiming to reach level 4 and above (just over half marks in the English Tests will achieve level 4). ReviseWise covers the key areas of English which will be tested.

How to get the most out of Key Stage 2 ReviseWise

- Help your child to work through the books. There are lots of tips from the ReviseWise owl to help with the answers and give advice.
- Encourage your child to watch (and re-watch) the videos. They bring the subject to life and explain what the Tests are all about.
- Is your child always glued to the computer? The CD-ROM takes children through questions step-by-step, with as much – or as little – help as they need along the way.
- If you're on the Internet, your child can visit the website for more learning fun. There's also a special section to help parents get to grips with the Tests and revision.

If you like, you can agree rewards with your child for successfully completing activities. See the chart at the back.

Using this book

Each page in this book offers questions, puzzles or activities which will help children confirm what they know and practise their skills in English ready for the KS2 Tests. The main points they need to know are highlighted at the top of each page. Some things may seem different from when you learned them. Ask the teacher if you're not sure.

Children can work steadily through the book, or head straight for the activities they know they need more practice in. At the end of each page, children can record their progress by marking their score on the pictures running up the right hand side of the page. They can circle or tick the picture showing the number of answers they have got right.

If children do the activities in this book in pencil, they can do them again later, either for repeat practice, or if they get any answers wrong. They can keep track of how much work they have done, and their scores, by filling in the score chart at the back of the book.

Answers

The Answers section at the back of this book gives the correct answers to straightforward questions. In the English Tests, not all answers are that simple, but you will fnd a guide to the kind of response that is expected so that you can judge whether your child has included the most important points.

Finally, please remember that the level you feel that your child achieves by answering the questions in this book can only give you a very general idea of the actual level he or she may achieve in the Tests.

Other resources for ReviseWise Challenge:

Maths quiz book ISBN 0 563 54219 5

Maths quiz video ISBN 0 563 54225 X

Science quiz book ISBN 0 563 54220 9

Science quiz video ISBN 0 563 54226 8

Spelling

Word endings

For most words which end in a vowel and a single consonant, double the consonant before adding ing/er/ed

rip – ripping   mad – madder   sip – sipped

For words ending in 'e', do not double. Drop the 'e' before adding ing/er/ed

smile – smiling   poke – poker   fine – fined

Add **ing**, then **er**, then **ed** to these words.

The vowels are a, e, i, o, u

	ing	er	ed
hop			
slip			
wrap			
flip			
pop			

5 points

Round 2

Match each word in the flower with a word on a bee.

Flower: tap, hat, hop, hope, ripe, dote, hate, rip, dot, tape

Bees: doted, hated, ripped, riper, hatter, dotted, taped, hoping, hopping, tapping

10 points

15 14 13 12 11 10 9 8 7 6 5 4 3 2 1

Circle your score!

Silent letters

Some words have silent letters in them which make no sound at all.

Look at these words, for example: **write** **hour**

Round 1

Fill in the silent letters in these words.

1 ___ r i g g l e

2 ___ n o t

3 r e i ___ n

4 ___ n o w l e d g e

5 ___ o n e s t

5 points

Right or -rong?

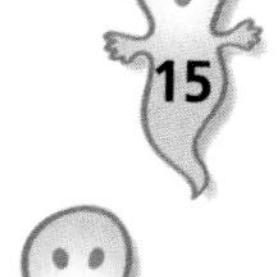

Fill in the answers to these clues. They all have a silent letter.

10 points

	Clue	Answer
1	a young sheep	l ___ ___ ___
2	lives in a haunted house	g ___ ___ ___ ___
3	food which comes in packets	b ___ ___ ___ ___ ___ ___
4	a knight's weapon	s ___ ___ ___ ___
5	comes after a question	a ___ ___ ___ ___ ___
6	prisoners were kept here	d ___ ___ ___ ___ ___ ___
7	four fingers and this	t ___ ___ ___ ___
8	sixty minutes	___ ___ ___ ___
9	the opposite of correct	___ ___ ___ ___ ___
10	you use this to cut	___ ___ ___ ___ ___

The last three begin with silent letters.

Circle the ghost with your score on it.

Plurals

These are the rules for making words plural:

- For many words, just add **s** — flower – flowers
- For words ending in s, x, ch and sh add **es** — box – boxes
- For many words ending in f or fe, drop the f or fe and add **ves** — leaf – leaves
- These words do not follow the **ves** rule: chiefs / cliffs / dwarfs / gulfs / oafs / muffs / reefs / roofs / handkerchiefs
- For words ending in y when the letter before is a consonant, drop the y and add **ies** — baby – babies
- For words ending in y when the letter before is a vowel, just add **s** — boy – boys
- For most words ending in o, which are to do with music, just add **s** — piano – pianos
- For other o words, add **es** — potato – potatoes
- Some words have plurals which are different words — tooth – teeth

Singular = one
Plural = more than one

Follow the rules and complete the crossword with plurals.

Across

2 table **6** knife
11 sister **12** pony
13 crocodile **16** class
17 army **18** man **19** foot
20 ray

Down

1 ox **3** bush **4** echo
5 dwarf **7** vase **8** fox
9 toy **10** piccolo **14** calf
15 chief

1 2 3 4 5 6 7 8 9 10 11 12 13 14 15 16 17 18 19 20

20 points

Which leaf has your score on it?

19 20 17 18 15 16 13 14 11 12 9 10 7 8 5 6 4 3 2 1

Misspelt words

There are some words which people always find hard to spell correctly. The only thing to do is to sit down and learn them. Use the 'Look Cover Write Check' way of learning them.

Underline the correct spelling.

1	neccessary	necessary	necesary
2	becos	becase	because
3	woz	was	wos
4	imediately	immediatly	immediately
5	thort	thought	thorght
6	although	allthough	althow
7	butiful	beautifull	beautiful
8	business	bisness	buisness
9	laff	laugh	lagh
10	meny	mene	many

10 points

Can you sort out the letters to make a word to fit each clue?

1	a part of something	i p e e c _ _ _ _ _
2	use a pen	r e w i t _ _ _ _ _
3	a weapon	o r w s d _ _ _ _ _
4	at the end	i n l l f y a _ _ _ _ _ _ _
5	happens only one time	n c o e _ _ _ _

5 points

Homophones

There are some words which sound the same but are spelled differently and have a different meaning. For instance

key - used to lock and unlock something

quay - a place for ships to load and unload

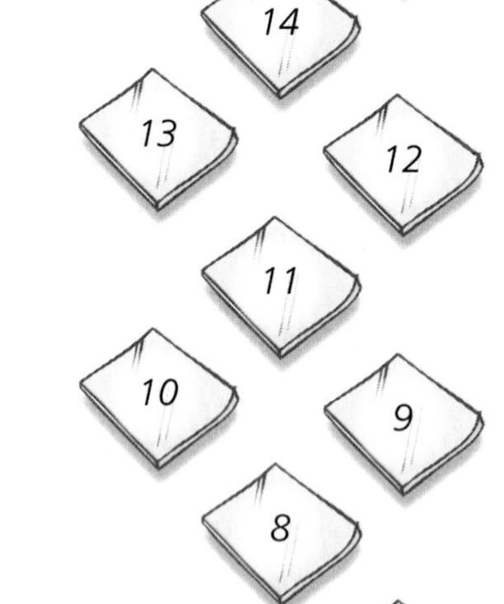

Use a dictionary to find out what the other words mean.

Round 1

Join the meaning to the correct word.

1	birth berth	bunk in a ship or train
2	draught draft	a stream of cold air
3	stake steak	a piece of meat
4	chord cord	thick string
5	allowed aloud	permission to do something

5 points

Round 2

Find the homophone in the word grid for each of these words

1 maize **2** pear

3 knead **4** ruff

5 vale **6** hare

7 pale **8** their

9 which **10** paws

10 points

a	y	b	o	h	d	l	c	n	r	v	a	q	l	p	x	n
r	s	t	c	a	d	o	x	p	a	u	s	e	z	a	n	t
e	g	w	f	i	s	t	w	m	n	l	a	t	o	i	y	k
b	n	i	z	r	o	u	g	h	i	f	v	g	r	r	u	l
e	t	t	f	z	u	m	x	v	b	e	x	f	l	y	z	a
v	i	c	n	p	q	b	l	m	v	p	s	o	r	x	f	g
a	t	h	e	r	e	z	n	c	e	d	h	o	f	k	p	l
q	x	b	f	j	n	r	u	a	i	z	c	b	z	d	f	k
v	i	v	a	h	p	b	d	l	l	p	u	d	k	p	v	s
b	n	w	c	j	r	z	p	n	z	l	w	n	u	a	x	c
f	o	l	n	e	e	d	s	i	r	g	l	x	t	i	p	d
i	r	x	e	l	a	c	m	a	z	e	h	s	b	l	z	t
k	t	z	g	n	v	x	k	u	c	a	y	m	o	r	d	y

Dropping the 'e'

Many words end in a silent 'e'.

love **white** **excite**

- When you add a suffix which begins with a vowel you drop the e.

loving **whitish** **excitable**

- When you add a suffix which begins with a consonant you keep the e.

lovely **whiteness** **excitement**

Not all words follow these rules.

- Words ending in ce or ge keep the e when **able** or **ous** is added.

change **changeable**

A suffix is added to the end of a word.

Use the rules above and add the suffixes in brackets to these words.

1 spite (ful) ____________ 2 amaze (ment) ____________

3 love (ing) ____________ 4 idle (ness) ____________

4 lone (ly) ____________ 6 fame (ous) ____________

7 sense (less) ____________ 8 wise (ly) ____________

9 stare (ing) ____________ 10 assure (ance) ____________

10 points

Using ALL the rules on this page, add the suffixes in brackets to these words.

1 desire (ous) ____________ 2 manage (able) ____________

3 elope (ment) ____________ 4 sure (ly) ____________

5 notice (able) ____________ 6 dine (ing) ____________

7 peace (able) ____________ 8 trace (able) ____________

9 advantage (ous) ____________ 10 courage (ous) ____________

10 points

20 19 18 17 16 15 14 13 12 11 10 9 8 7 6 5 4 3 2 1

Quick spelling quiz

1 Add **ing** to sleep ________

2 Write a word with a silent **h** ________

3 Write the plural of **leaf** ________

4 Which is correct:
business or **buisness?** ________

5 Write the homophone for **stake** ________

6 Add the suffix **able** to **notice** ________

7 Write the plural of **match** ________

8 Add **ing** to **smile** ________

9 Write a word with a silent **w** ________

10 Which is correct:
beautifull or **beautiful?** ________

11 Write a word with a silent **k** ________

12 Write the plural of **donkey** ________

13 Add the suffix **ly** to love ________

14 Write the singular of **ponies** ________

15 Sort the letters to make a word meaning a place for storing things
u c b r a p o d ________

16 Which is correct:
because or **becos?** ________

17 Add the suffix **ous** to **outrage** ________

18 Write the singular of **policemen** ________

19 Sort the letters to make a word which means a place from which you borrow books
r l a r i y b ________

20 Write the homophone for **there** ________

Score [ ]

20 points

Time yourself!

Apostrophe for missing letters

An apostrophe is a punctuation mark which shows when letters have been missed out.

we are	**-**	**we're**	**The 'a' has been missed out.**
I have	**-**	**I've**	**The 'ha' has been missed out.**

Words with missing letters are called contractions.

We use contractions when we write speech.

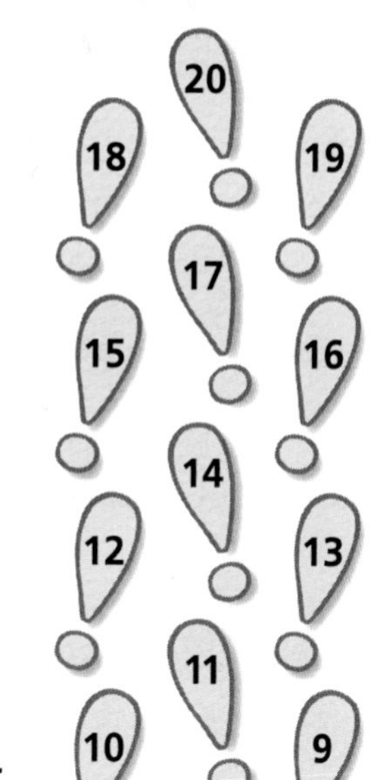

Match the words with their contractions.

10 points

1	have not	we'll
2	will not	don't
3	you have	haven't
4	we will	you'd
5	it is	I'm
6	they are	it's
7	should not	won't
8	I am	shouldn't
9	you would	you've
10	do not	they're

Round 2

Sort out each group of muddled letters to make 2 words.
Write each one as a contraction and add the apostrophe.

		2 words	contraction
1	h d e a h	_ _ _ _ _	_ _ _
2	u l t s e	_ _ _ _ _	_ _ _ _
3	e h w d a	_ _ _ _ _	_ _ _
4	d d n i t o	_ _ _ _ _ _	_ _ _ _ _
5	n h s o a t	_ _ _ _ _ _	_ _ _ _ _

10 points

Apostrophe s for possession

We use an apostrophe **s ('s)** to show something is owned by or belongs to somebody or something.

Look: the lead belonging to the dog = the dog's lead

Where there is more than one owner, add ' after the s.

the cats' tails

If the owners do not end in s, add **'s**.

the children's ball

What is the other use for the apostrophe?

Round 1

Follow the lines to find out what each child has.

Write each one like this: Gary's boat

Kim	apple	______
Tom	jumper	______
Sima	book	______
Lee	watch	______
Sulim	joke	______

5 points

Round 2

Each of these owners has a cake.

Look carefully to see if the owner is singular or plural.

Write each one like this: the girls' cake

Is the apostrophe before or after the s?

Sally ______	clowns ______
men ______	boys ______
ladies ______	baker ______
teacher ______	nurses ______
winner ______	gardeners ______

10 points

15 14 13 12 11 10 9 8 7 6 5 4 3 2 1

Direct speech

Direct speech uses speech marks. Here are the rules:

- speech marks go at the beginning and the end of the spoken words
- the punctuation at the end of the spoken words – comma, full stop exclamation mark, question mark – comes inside the speech marks
- begin a new paragrpah on a new line when a different person speaks.

"How are you today?" asked Mr Clark.

" Very well, thank you," replied Mrs Timms. " How are you keeping?"

"Can't complain," said Mr Clark.

Round 1

Try not to use 'said' every time.

Look at the spoken words in the speech bubbles.
Write them in direct speech and show who is saying what by adding **said, replied, asked** and so on, and putting in a speaker's name.

What time is it?

About half past six.

I've lost my book!

Where did you have it last?

4 points

10

9

8

7

6

5

Round 2

Add speech marks and any other missing punctuation

6 points

4

3

2

1

1 That was a very strange story murmured Fred
2 I don't want to play yelled Sam.
3 When did you last feed the dog asked Mum
4 I went to the shop explained Becky It was shut
5 Mrs Brown shouted Look out
6 Have you any idea where I put my spectacles asked Grandad

Indirect speech

Indirect speech is when you write about what someone has said but you do not use the actual spoken words.

direct speech	indirect speech
↓	↓
"I'd like pizza for tea," said Jane.	**Jane said that she would like pizza for tea.**

Indirect speech does not need speech marks.

Round 1 Write these direct speech sentences as indirect speech.

Remember, you don't need speech marks!

1 "What sort of pizza would you like?" asked Dad.

____

2 "Cheese and tomato," replied Jane.

____

3 "I hate cheese and tomato," exclaimed James.

____

4 "Well, what sort would you like?" asked Dad.

____

5 "Ham and pineapple, I think," decided James.

____

5 points

Write these indirect speech sentences as direct speech.

Remember your speech marks.

1 Dad said that there were no pizzas in the freezer.

____

2 He wanted to know what Jane and James would have instead.

____

3 Jane decided she would have pasta.

____

4 James wanted to buy fish and chips.

____

5 Dad thought it would be a good idea to have salad.

____

5 points

4

Question marks and exclamation marks

Most sentences end in full stops but there are times when you need a **question mark** or an **exclamation mark.**

- A question mark comes at the end of a question.

  "Where are you going?" asked Fred.
- An exclamation mark can be used when someone is shouting or excited or they are saying something suprising or strange.

  "I've just seen a flying saucer!" exclaimed Gemma.

Round 1

Add a question mark or an exclamation mark to the end of these sentences.

5 points

Is the bus late

This ice cream tastes horrible

That tree is going to fall

If you do that I will be really angry

What is that

Round 2

Sort the words in the box into those you can use with questions and those you can use with exclamations.

request roar beg yell enquire

shout plead cheer ask cry

demand scream sob implore wonder

questions

____
____
____
____
____
____
____
____

exclamations

____
____
____
____
____
____
____

15 points

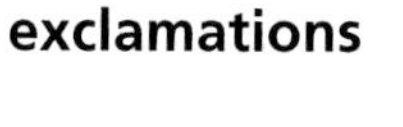

Quick punctuation quiz

Time yourself

1. Write the contraction of **would not.** ____________
2. Write the **cat belonging to Tom** using an apostrophe ____________
3. Write this with the speech marks: **My name is Mina she said.** ____________
4. Do you need a question mark or an exclamation mark? "Go away [ ] " yelled Sara ____________
5. Put in the apostrophe: **I can't do that.** ____________
6. Write the contraction of **I am** ____________
7. Make this indirect speech: **John said, " I'm going to be late!"** ____________
8. Do you need a question mark or an exclamation mark? **Is this your book** [ ] ____________
9. Write **the boat belonging to the men** using an apostrophe. ____________
10. Write **mustn't** as two words. ____________
11. Write this using an apostrophe: **the car belonging to the family** ____________
12. Make this direct speech: **The old lady said she was cold.** ____________
13. Write **didn't** as two words. ____________
14. Write the contraction of he **cannot.** ____________
15. Make **the child's toy** plural. ____________
16. Write the contraction of **they will.** ____________
17. Write this as indirect speech: **"Is that letter for me?" enquired Sam.** ____________
18. Write **they've** as two words. ____________
19. Write the contraction of **she would.** ____________
20. Write **the rattles belonging to the babies** using an apostrophe. ____________

Score [ ]

20 points

Verb tenses

Verbs have different tenses. Note how they change.

Present tense – happening now **I smile, he smiles**

Past tense – has happened **we smiled, they smiled**

Future tense – will happen **I shall smile, we shall smile**
you will smile, she will smile

Complete the chart.

Verb	Present tense		Past tense		Future tense	
to mend	I	mend	we	______	you	______
to look	we	______	he	______	she	______
to paint	you	______	I	______	we	will paint
to clean	he	______	they	______	I	______
to like	it	______	you	liked	they	______

15 points

Complete each sentence with the correct form of the verb in brackets.

1 Tomorrow I ______________ to the library (to go)
2 Yesterday they ______________ the car. (to wash)
3 We ______________ the picnic later. (to eat)
4 You ______________ over that wall before. (to jump)
5 It ______________ every day last week. (to rain)

5 points

Past tense

You usually write stories in the **past tense.**

Lots of verbs make their past tense by adding ed: walk – walked.

Lots of verbs do not follow this rule: sleep – slept

Fill in the crossword by changing these verbs into the **past tense**.

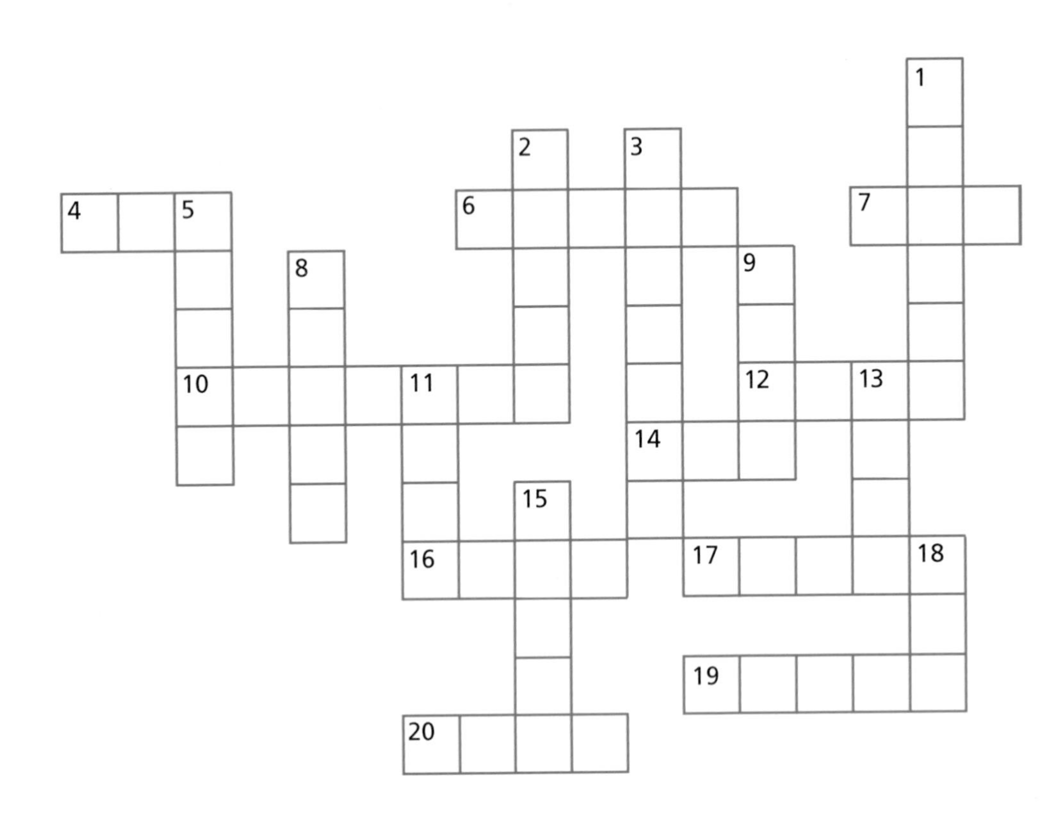

Across

4 see **6** hear **7** dig **10** think
12 leave **14** have **16** weep
17 can **19** find **20** fly

Down

1 buy **2** mean **3** bring
5 write **8** drive **9** tell
11 grow **13** fall
15 speak **18** do

None of these verbs use ed to make their past tense.

20 points

20 19 18 17 16 15 14 13 12 11 10 9 8 7 6 5 4 3 2 1

The verb to be

The verb **to be** is very useful because it helps you make other tenses.

Present – happening now	**I sit**	**I am sitting**
	He sits	**He is sitting**
	We sit	**We are sitting**
Past – has happened	**I jumped**	**I was jumping**
	You jumped	**You were jumping**
	We jumped	**We were jumping**

Put these present tense verbs into the past tense.

1 you are looking ______________________

2 I am laughing ______________________

3 it is barking ______________________

4 we are talking ______________________

5 they are clapping ______________________

5 points

Put these past tense verbs into the present tense.

1 they were digging ______________________

2 you were crying ______________________

3 it was raining ______________________

4 she was singing ______________________

5 I was writing ______________________

5 points

Adjectives

If you get stuck, use a thesaurus. Look up the word in red.

Adjectives are describing words which give more information about nouns and pronouns.

Adjectives can come before or after the noun or pronoun.

The **strong** man lifted the **huge** tree trunk.

The man was **strong**. He easily lifted the tree trunk, which was **huge**.

Adjectives make our writing more interesting.

Round 1

Find an adjective that can be used to describe each word in the set.

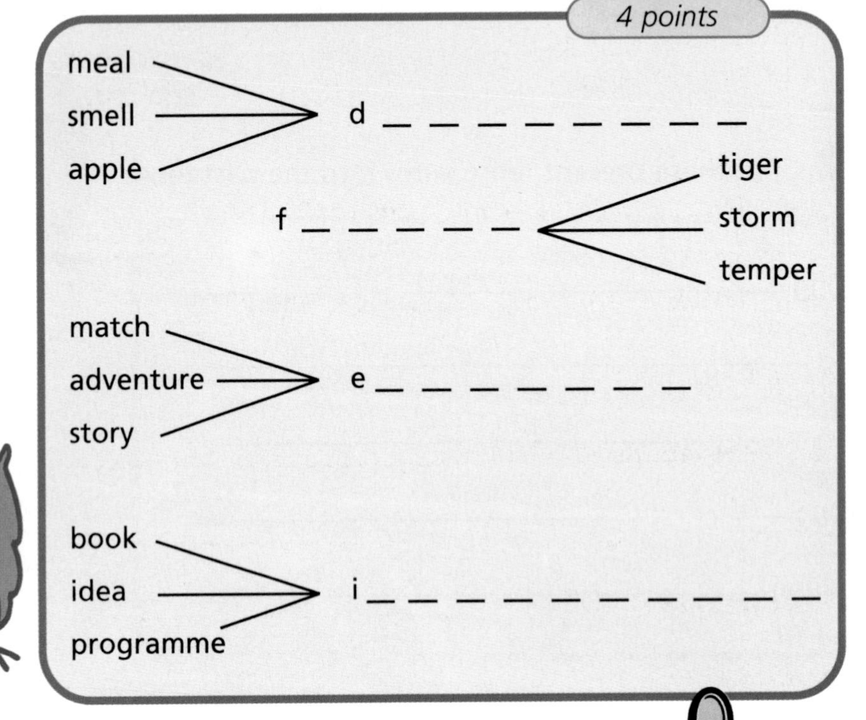

Round 2

Sort out these jumbled adjectives which mean the same as the word in red.

Clue: Each word begins with the bold letter.

sad	h**u**pyapn	c**d**awnots **downcast**	per**d**sdsee
small	ny**i**t	li**s**htg	a**m**teainiru
hot	ng**b**riun	lino**b**gi	ryei**f**
pretty	v**l**oeyl	taivtrcaet	ari**f**

11 points

15 14 13 12 11 10 9 8 7

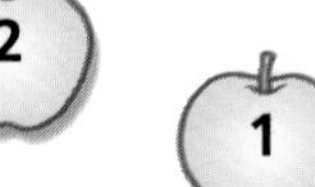

Adverbs

Adverbs tell us more about **how**, **where**, and **when** things happen.

They give us more information about verbs.

The tree fell **slowly.**	**Slowly** tells us **how.**
The tree fell **here.**	**Here** tells us **where.**
The tree fell **yesterday.**	**Yesterday** tells us **when.**

Adverbs can be formed from adjectives.

adjective	**adverb**
hopeful	hopefully
weary	wearily

Round 1

Underline the adverb in each sentence.

Does the advert tell us about 'how', 'where' or 'when'?

1 I will go to the shops later. ______________________

2 The train screeched noisily to a halt. ______________________

3 It will rain today. ______________________

4 Have you looked everywhere? ______________________

5 The dog growled angrily. ______________________

5 points

Round 2

Make these adjectives into adverbs.

1 skilful ______________________

2 harsh ______________________

3 true ______________________

4 frantic ______________________

5 full ______________________

5 points

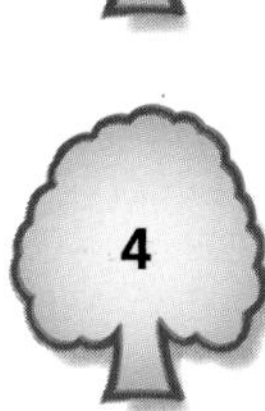

Conjunctions

Conjunctions are very useful words.

They are used to join short sentences to make them more interesting.

She closed the window. She left the house.

She closed the window **before** she left the house.

She closed the window **when** she left the house.

Copy the conjunctions carefully and learn to spell them.

In this word search you will find 10 useful conjunctions which you can use to improve your writing.

The first letter of each one is given to help you.

b _ _   s _   a f _ _ r

a l t _ _ _   g _   w _ _ _

u _ l _ s s   i _   t h _ _

a _ _   b _ c _ _ _ _

10 points

These words are useful conjunctions: but, if, so, because, although, until, which, and.

u	r	b	e	c	a	u	s	e	l	v	a	w	l	o
n	a	g	o	a	l	u	o	v	d	u	g	w	e	x
l	y	w	f	l	t	c	u	k	a	i	z	h	q	n
e	t	n	p	i	h	s	c	d	a	f	t	e	r	h
s	r	b	d	w	o	t	u	b	v	p	m	n	l	q
s	o	f	h	c	u	k	s	i	l	f	h	y	f	l
a	z	e	m	j	g	x	a	r	b	l	x	r	j	p
q	e	q	o	t	h	e	n	c	w	b	u	t	s	n
d	f	o	l	k	x	g	d	j	w	k	m	o	z	v
e	z	r	b	y	s	y	p	t	n	h	t	j	u	m

Quick grammar quiz

Time yourself

1 Write the future tense of **I sing.** ______________

2 Write the past tense of **they leave.** ______________

3 Which is correct: I **am** diving. I **is** diving ______________

4 Write the adjective in this sentence:
The old man shuffled along. ______________

5 Does this adverb describe how, when or where:
beautifully ______________

6 Write a conjunction which could join these sentences:
The dog barked. He was let out of the house. ______________

7 Write the present tense of **he laughed.** ______________

8 Write this in the past tense: **You are running.** ______________

9 Which is correct: **We was laughing.** ______________
We **were** laughing. ______________

10 Does this adverb describe how when or where:
anywhere ______________

11 Write the past tense of **we skip.** ______________

12 Write **clumsy** as an adverb. ______________

13 Write a conjunction which could join these two sentences:
I wanted to go out. It was raining. ______________

14 Write the adjective in this sentence:
The rose in the vase was beautiful. ______________

15 Write the past tense of **you write.** ______________

16 Write **truthful** as an adverb. ______________

17 Write this in the present tense: **It was raining.** ______________

18 Does this adverb describe how, when or where: ______________
occasionally ______________

19 Write a conjunction which could join these sentences:
The flower was dead. I threw it out. ______________

20 Write the past tense of **it blows.** ______________

Score ☐

20 points

Synonyms

Synonyms are words that mean the same, or nearly the same, as each other.

modern: new up-to-date

trick: joke prank

Round 1

Write the pairs of synonyms in the box.

careful	**exciting**
toss	**rarely**
join	**attentive**
seldom	**throw**
thrilling	**connect**

1 ______________ and ______________

2 ______________ and ______________

3 ______________ and ______________

4 ______________ and ______________

5 ______________ and ______________

5 points

Round 2

Write the word in the brackets which is the synonym of the word on the left.

1 rude (polite / cross / impolite) ______________

2 save (ignore / rescue / smear) ______________

3 increase (expand / manage / destroy) ______________

4 method (medium / system / clutter) ______________

5 secret (wisdom / notice / hidden) ______________

6 tender (gentle / fierce / stupid) ______________

7 valuable (different / rare / handy) ______________

8 average (normal / pleasing / extreme) ______________

9 district (channel / region / vacant) ______________

10 enough (simple / void / sufficient) ______________

10 points

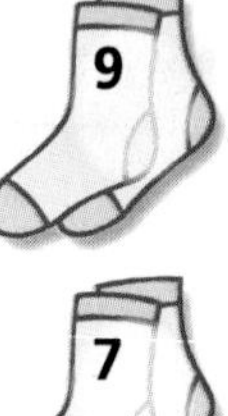

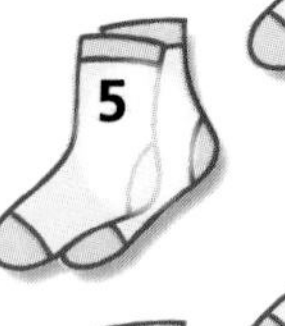

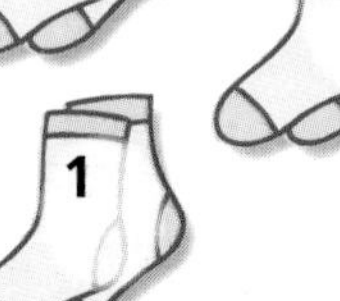

Over-used words

Some words are used too often: eg said, nice

You can think of more interesting words: eg mumbled, delicious

Words which mean the same, or nearly the same, are called synonyms.

In each letter square there are five synonyms for the word in the balloon.

Find the words and circle them.

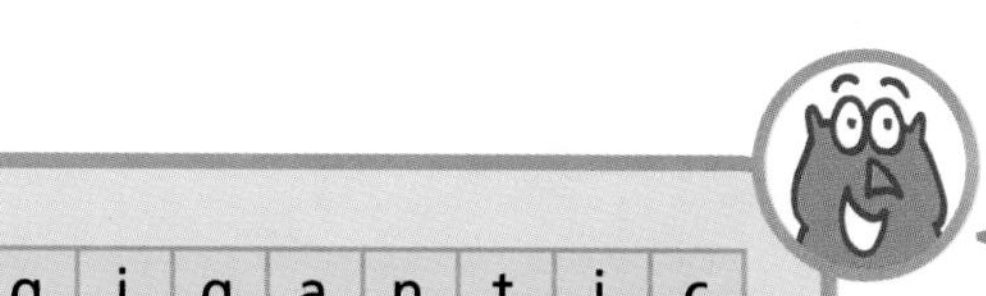

Find synonyms for the words in the balloons.

big

g	i	g	a	n	t	i	c
r	h	l	u	v	o	f	g
s	u	b	k	j	u	w	r
g	g	l	a	r	g	e	e
k	e	r	a	k	j	x	a
m	a	s	s	i	v	e	t

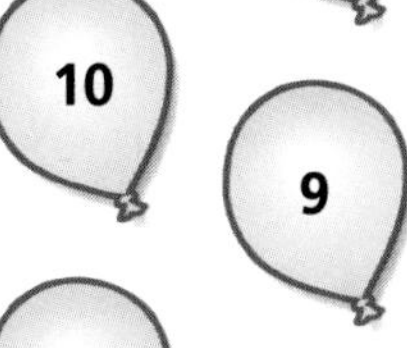

Have you found five synonyms?

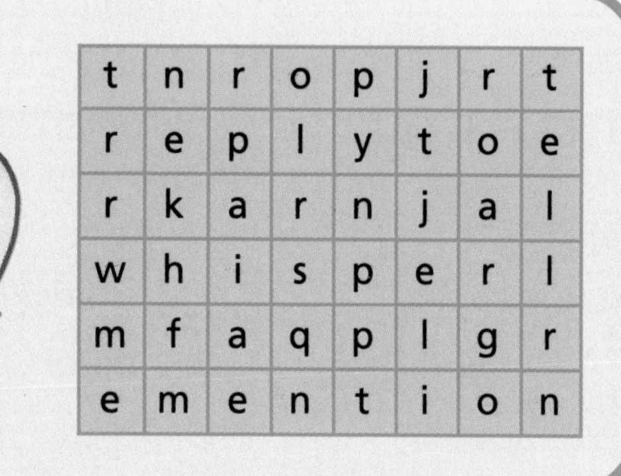

say

t	n	r	o	p	j	r	t
r	e	p	l	y	t	o	e
r	k	a	r	n	j	a	l
w	h	i	s	p	e	r	l
m	f	a	q	p	l	g	r
e	m	e	n	t	i	o	n

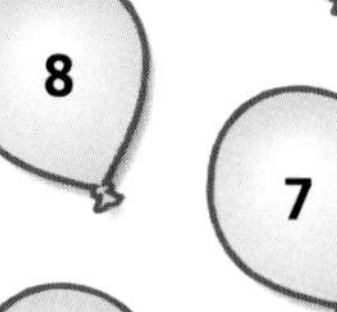

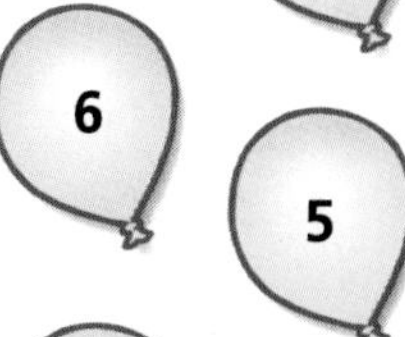

run

g	m	d	a	s	h	i	p
e	b	l	g	c	o	l	j
r	q	m	h	u	r	r	y
a	p	f	c	r	o	u	l
c	r	x	j	r	v	s	e
e	g	q	f	y	v	h	k

15 points

Antonyms

Antonyms are words with opposite meanings.

hot – cold

wet – dry

Many words make their opposites by adding a prefix.

trust – **dis**trust sure – **un**sure

A prefix is letters added to the beginning of a word.

Join each word in Box 1 with its antonym in Box 2.

Box 1	Box 2
partner	perfect
seldom	rough
faulty	wander
smooth	often
settle	rival

These antonyms are not made with a prefix.

5 points

Complete the word webs by writing the antonym for each word in the box. Two have been done for you.

lucky	appear	selfish	respect
	honour	kind	
usual	approve	true	agree

10 points

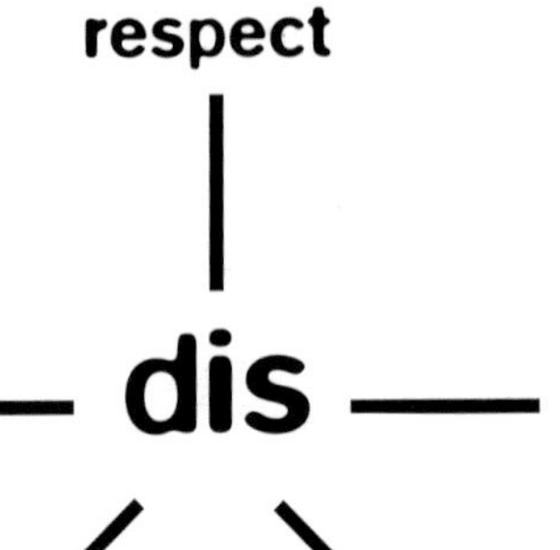

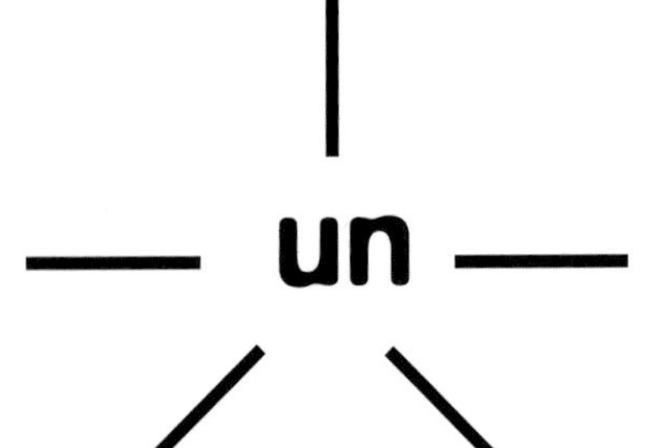

15 14 13 12 11 10 9 8 7 6 5 4 3 2 1

Compound words

Compound words are made by adding two words together.

play + time = playtime moon + light = moonlight

Make 10 or more compound words by joining together any two words in this box. For example, butter + fly = butterfly. You can use each word more than once.

head rain
man ball
stair
sun
snow
shelf
coat
light
foot
fly
butter
flower
cup fire
bed
case jacket book

10 9 8 7 6 5 4 3 2 1

_______________ _______________

_______________ _______________

_______________ _______________

_______________ _______________

_______________ _______________

10 points

Word families

Prefixes and suffixes are added to the root word to make family words.

Words can be grouped in families.

Word families have a simple word – called the root word – from which other words grow.

Root word	**Word family**
like	liking / liked / likeness / likeable
	dislike / unlikely

Put the words in the box in their family group.

unhappy wisdom happiness
happily unwise

happy	**wise**

5 points

Add three words to each family group.

Watch your spelling!

1 luck ______ ______ ______

2 use ______ ______ ______

3 time ______ ______ ______

4 sound ______ ______ ______

5 kind ______ ______ ______

15 points

20 19 18 17 16 15 14 13 12 11 10 9 8 7 6 5 4 3 2 1

Quick vocabulary quiz

Time yourself

1 Write a synonym beginning with **s** for **ill** ______

2 Write a more interesting word for **big** ______

3 Write the antonym for **often** ______

4 Add a word to **night** to make a compound word ______

5 Write the root word of **untrustworthy** ______

6 Write a synonym beginning with **g** for **protect** ______

7 Use a prefix to write the antonym for **wise** ______

8 Write the root word of **dutifully** ______

9 Add a word to **snow** to make a compound word ______

10 Write a synonym beginning with **c** for **sure** ______

11 Write a more interesting word for **sad** ______

12 Write the root word for **inescapable** ______

13 Add a word to **hedge** to make a compound word ______

14 Write the antonym for **laugh** ______

15 Put a word in front of **man** to make a compound word ______

16 Use a prefix to write the antonym for **worthy** ______

17 Write a more interesting word for **pretty** ______

18 Use a prefix to write the antonym for **allow** ______

19 Put a word in front of **fly** to make a compound word ______

20 Write a more interesting word for **said** ______

How did you do?

Score ______

20 points

Be the teacher!

This is your chance to use a red pen and find the mistakes other people have made!

Read each box carefully and then look at the sentences to find the mistakes.

Put a circle around any mistake you find and then correct it – just like a teacher!

its or it's?

its	=	belonging to	The dog emptied its bowl.
it's	=	it is	It's a beautiful morning.

Look carefully. Three of the sentences are correct!

1 "Its already five o'clock!" moaned Ali.

2 The bus had come to a halt because its engine was smoking.

3 The dog made a tremendous noise and it's barking woke me up.

4 I like the cherry tree with it's beautiful blossom.

5 If it's fine tomorrow, we'll go to the beach.

6 Its very unusual to get snow in summer.

7 The house was deserted and all its windows were broken.

8 I am really excited because its my birthday tomorrow!

9 The football is lost so its the end of the game.

10 The sandcastle lost it's walls when the wave came.

10 points

10 9 8 7 6 5 4 3 2 1

whose or who's?

whose	=	belonging to	I know a boy whose dad is an astronaut!
who's	=	who is	I know a man who's an astronaut!
		who has	I know an astronaut who's been to the moon!

Remember, some of the sentences could be right.

1 I know who's coat that is.

2 The boy whose riding the new bike is my friend.

3 The child who's crying, fell over in the playground.

4 "Whose got the tickets?" asked dad.

5 "Whose going to make a cup of tea?" asked Mum.

5 points

there, their or they're?

there	=	• a place word	I put the book there.
		• often comes before is, are, was were	There were only two apples left in the bowl.
their	=	belonging to	Their mother was meeting them after school.
they're	=	they are	They're going to the park after school.

Look carefully. One of these sentences is correct!

3

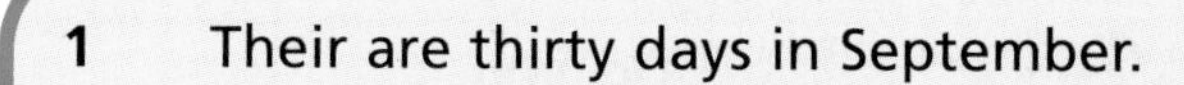

1 Their are thirty days in September.

2 There was a heavy storm in the night.

3 "I'm sure their is a quicker way," said Paul.

4 There bags were very heavy.

5 They put up they're hands when they knew the answer.

5 points

were or where?

where	=	a place word	Do you know where it is?
were	=	past tense of **are**	We are playing today.
			We were playing yesterday.

Where were the mistakes?

1 What where you doing yesterday?
2 He hid the treasure where no one would find it.
3 Although they where cold, they wanted to finish building the snowman.
4 Were is the cricket bat?
5 "I'm sure your book will be were you left it," said the teacher.

5 points

no or know?

no	=	opposite of yes none/not any	"No, I would not like any juice," said Henry. There are no tickets left.
know	=	having knowledge of something	I know the answer to that question.

Do you 'no' or 'know' the answers?

1 "I no what I'm doing!" snapped John.
2 There must be no talking during the test.
3 There are know clouds in the sky today.
4 "Do you no the time?" asked the old lady.
5 There is know reason to be frightened.

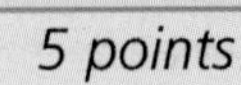
5 points

your or you're?

your	=	belonging to	Your hands are very dirty.
you're	=	you are	You're going to wash those hands before you eat!

1. "You're work is very good," said the teacher.
2. You can find you're way by using the map.
3. If your not well you should stay in bed.
4. I really enjoyed you're birthday party.
5. Your bicycle has a puncture.

5 points

I hope you're good at your spelling!

two, to or too?

two	=	the number 2	We have two eyes and two ears.
to	=	this can be used in many ways	I went to the shops.
			Does she have to?
			It's not clear to me.
too	=	as well	I want one, too.
		more than enough	It was too hot in the sun.

So, if the word you need isn't two or too, then it must be to!

1. The shop opens in two hours.
2. It will be two late to go soon.
3. Only too days until our holidays!
4. The dog wanted too chase the cat.
5. If we want too catch the train, we must leave now.

5 points

To – too – two? Sounds like my call.

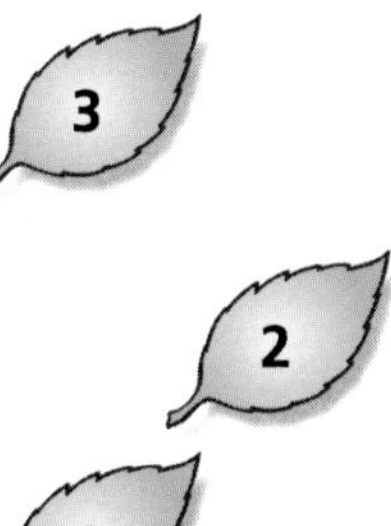

Passages 1 and 2

Now you need to think about everything you have learned in this book by working through these quizzes.

In **each** of the following four passages there are **15 mistakes**.

Look carefully at the spelling and punctuation. Can you spot them?

Get a red pen and start marking!

Passage 1

Their was going to be a fare at the edge of town?

Sam and Tom were hopping to go in the morning.

How long can we stay for? "asked Tom."

"About an our," said Mum.

"I have'nt got any money," moaned Sam.

"I will give you some," said Mum, but you mustn't spend it all on sweets."

The boy's where very excited and they couldn't weight until it was time too go.

When they woke up the next morning, the sun was shineing.

They got out of bed and eated a good breakfast before they set off. They was very careful crossing the road and they arrived just as the gates were opening.

Passage 2

I remember my first day in school. It was when I were five years old? My teacher was called Mrs Lowry.

Although I was very little, I feeled very grown up as I walkd into the class room.

I was siting in the front next to a boy called Paul. We spent the first half of the morning writeing the letters of the alphabet. We had fifteen minutes for playtime and we where given a drink of milk and a biscit.

After playtime. Mrs Lowry read us a story about a family of foxs and a hair with very long ears. We then had to draw a picture but I could'nt draw the fox very well. Pauls picture was great. He said that "he liked to draw".

Passages 3 and 4

Passage 3

Mrs Horner wanted to buy some fruit. She went into the little shop and speaked to Mr Long.

"Good morning, Mr Long, she said. "I hope yo'uve some fresh fruit today."

"Of course, Mrs Horner. My fruit is allways fresh."

"Id like some apples and pairs," she said. "Those strawberrys look good. I buyed some of those last week and they was delicious."

"Its the write time of the year for them," remarked Mr Long. "How meny apples would you like?"

'Six please," replied Mrs Horner. "Ill take some bananas, to. I is very fond of banana sandwiches."

Passage 4

Not a sound could be herd in the wood. Their was a covering of snow on the ground and the leafs on the trees was white.

Suddenly, the snow beginned to fall again from the heavy, grey clouds. A small badger scurried through the trees on it's way home. It stoped by a large oak tree and sniffed the air. It sensed danger! Were was it comeing from. The badger did'nt wait too find out. It runned quickly into the nearby bushs and made know movement until the danger had passed.

Have you missed anything? There are 15 mistakes in each passage.

Multi Quiz 1

Time yourself

1 Add **ing** to **rip**. ____________

2 Write the plural of **knife**. ____________

3 Add punctuation to this: ____________

Are you hurt cried the boy. ____________

4 Add **able** to **peace**. ____________

5 Write the silent letter in **ghost**. ____________

6 Do you need a question mark or an exclamation mark: ____________

"I don't know ☐ " yelled Nathan. ____________

7 Which is the correct spelling: **neccesary** or **necessary**? ____________

8 Write the correct word from the brackets: (**Whose** / **Who's**) going to watch a video? ____________

9 Write the homophone of **which**. ____________

10 Add ed to **wrap**. ____________

11 Write a synonym beginning with **g** for **tender**. ____________

12 Write **the bone belonging to the dog** with an apostrophe. ____________

13 Write the antonym of **usual** using a prefix. ____________

14 Write the present tense of **he looked**. ____________

15 Write the root word of **impolitely**. ____________

16 Write the contraction of **I have**. ____________

17 Write the correct word from the brackets: They put (**there** / **their**) books on the table. ____________

18 Write the past tense of **I am riding**. ____________

19 Make this sentence plural: **The lady's hat was very colourful.** ____________

20 Write this in indirect speech: **"May I go now?" asked Billy.** ____________

Score ☐

Multi Quiz 2

Time yourself

1 Write the past tense of **I sleep**. ______

2 Write the silent letter in **thumb**. ______

3 Write **the toys belonging to the children** using an apsotrophe. ______

4 Add **ous** to **courage**. ______

5 Write a synonym beginning with **a** for **funny**. ______

6 Write the plural of **foot**. ______

7 Write the antonym of **agree** using a prefix. ______

8 Write the contraction of **will not**. ______

9 Write the root word of **unmanageable**. ______

10 Add **ed** to **flip**. ______

11 Write this in indirect speech: **"The lion has escaped!"shouted the zoo keeper.** ______

12 Write the correct word from the brackets: (**Were** / **Where** are you going?) ______

13 Write the homophone of **pail**. ______

14 Write a word with a silent **k**. ______

15 Add punctuation to this sentence: **Look out shouted the policeman** ______

16 Make this sentence singular: **The oxen's carts were heavy.** ______

17 Add **ing** to **wave**. ______

18 Do you need a question mark or an exclamation mark? **"Can we find out ☐ " enquired Ben.** ______

19 Write the correct word from the brackets: We **were** / **where** very late for school. ______

20 Which is the correct spelling? **although** or **allthough**? ______

Score ☐

Multi Quiz 3

Time yourself

1. Write **the coats belonging to the babies** using an apostrophe. ____________
2. Write the antonym of **smooth** beginning with **r**. ____________
3. Write the correct word from the brackets: (**Your / You're**) in trouble now! ____________
4. Write the past tense of **you are playing** ____________
5. Add **er** to **bat**. ____________
6. Write a synonym beginning with **e** for **thrilling**. ____________
7. Add punctuation to this: **That was very funny laughed Sulim.** ____________
8. Write the root word of **disinterestedly**. ____________
9. Write the plural of **echo**. ____________
10. Write the correct word from the brackets: I think (**its / it's**) paw is hurt. ____________
11. Write the homophone of **allowed**. ____________
12. Which is the correct spelling: **was** or **wos**? ____________
13. Write the silent letter in **dungeon**. ____________
14. Make this sentence plural: **The child's poem is very good.** ____________
15. Add **able** to **notice**. ____________
16. Write the correct word from the brackets: It is (**to / two / too**) cold to go outside. ____________
17. Add **ed** to **like**. ____________
18. Write this as indirect speech: **"It was the best film I've ever seen," said Linda.** ____________
19. Write the contraction of **we shall**. ____________
20. Which is the correct spelling: **becos** or **because**? ____________

Score ____

Answers

Spelling section

page 6

round 1

hopping	hopper	hopped
slipping	slipper	slipped
wrapping	wrapper	wrapped
flipping	flipper	flipped
popping	popper	popped

round 2

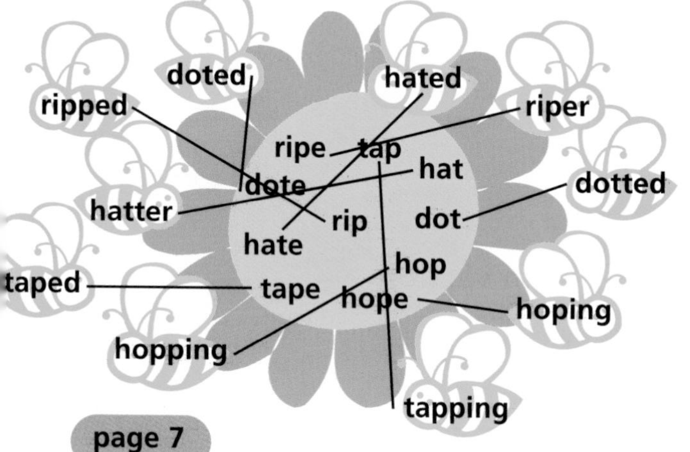

page 7

round 1

1 wriggle **2** knot **3** reign
4 knowledge **5** honest

round 2

1 lamb
2 ghost
3 biscuits
4 sword
5 answer
6 dungeon
7 thumb
8 hour
9 wrong
10 knife

page 8

					[1] o										
					x		[2] t	a	[3] b	l	[4] e	s			[5] d
					e				u		c				w
				[6] k	n	i	[7] v	e	s		h		[8] f		a
							a		h		o		o		r
							s		e		e		x		f
			[9] t		[10] p		e		[11] s	i	s	t	e	r	s
		[12] p	o	n	i	e	s						s		
			y		c										
			s		[13] c	r	o	[14] c	o	d	i	l	e	s	
					o			a							
			[15] c		l		[16] c	l	a	s	s	e	s		
			h		o			v							
[17] a	r	m	i	e	s		[18] m	e	n						
			e					s							
			[19] f	e	e	t									
[20] r	a	y	s												

page 9

round 1

1 necessary **2** because **3** was
4 immediately **5** thought **6** although
7 beautiful **8** business **9** laugh **10** many

round 2

1 piece **2** write **3** sword
4 finally **5** once

page 10

round 1

1 berth - bunk in ship or train
2 draught - stream of cold air
3 steak - piece of meat
4 cord - thick string
5 allowed - permission to do something

round 2

a	y	b	o	h	d	l	c	n	r	v	a	q	l	p	x	n
r	s	t	c	a	d	o	x	p	a	u	s	e	z	a	n	t
e	g	w	f	i	s	t	w	m	n	l	a	t	o	i	y	k
b	n	i	z	r	o	u	g	h	i	f	v	g	r	r	u	l
e	t	t	f	z	u	m	x	v	b	e	x	f	l	y	z	a
v	i	c	n	p	q	b	l	m	v	p	s	o	r	x	f	g
a	t	h	e	r	e	z	n	c	e	d	h	o	f	k	p	l
q	x	b	f	j	n	r	u	a	i	z	c	b	z	d	f	k
v	i	v	a	h	p	b	d	l	l	p	u	d	k	p	v	s
b	n	w	c	j	r	z	p	n	z	l	w	n	u	a	x	c
f	o	l	n	e	e	d	s	i	r	g	l	x	t	i	p	d
i	r	x	e	l	a	c	m	a	z	e	h	s	b	l	z	t
k	t	z	g	n	v	x	k	u	c	a	y	m	o	r	d	y

1 maize **2** pear **3** knead **4** ruff **5** vale
6 hare **7** pale **8** their **9** which **10** paws

page 11

round 1

1 spiteful **2** amazement
3 loving **4** idleness
5 lonely **6** famous
7 senseless **8** wisely
9 staring **10** assurance

round 2

1 desirous **2** manageable
3 elopement **4** surely
5 noticeable **6** dining
7 peaceable **8** traceable
9 advantageous **10** courageous

page 12

1 sleeping
2 hour / ghost / heir / heiress / honest
3 leaves
4 business
5 steak
6 noticeable
7 matches
8 smiling
9 write / wrap / wrapping / wrapped / wreck / wring / wrong / wren / wrestle / written / writing / wrist / wriggle
10 beautiful
11 knife / knee / knot / kneel / know / knew / knowledge / knuckle / knit / knitting / knitted / knock / knocking / knocked / knead / kneading /kneaded / knave
12 donkeys
13 lovely
14 pony
15 cupboard
16 because
17 outrageous
18 policeman
19 library
20 their

Punctuation section

page 13

round 1

have not - haven't
will not - won't
you have - you've
we will - we'll
it is - it's
they are - they're
should not - shouldn't
I am - I'm
you would - you'd
do not - don't

round 2

1 he had he'd

2 let us let's

3 we had we'd

4 did not didn't

5 has not hasn't

page 14

round 1

Sima's apple

Lee's jumper

Tom's book

Kim's watch

Sulim's joke

Round 2

Sally's cake	the clowns' cake
the men's cake	the boys' cake
the ladies' cake	the baker's cake
the teacher's cake	the nurses' cake
the winner's cake	the gardeners' cake

page 15 **round 1**

"What time is it?" asked Ben.

"About half past six," replied Kim.

"I've lost my book!" shouted Becky.

"Where did you have it last?" asked Sue.

NB Your child may have written 'said' each time, which is correct, but encourage him / her to use words such as 'replied' / 'asked' etc in direct speech.

round 2

1 "That was a very strange story," murmured Fred.

2 "I don't want to play!" yelled Sam.

3 "When did you last feed the dog?" asked Mum.

4 "I went to the shop," explained Becky. "It was shut."

5 Mrs Brown shouted, "Look out!"

6 "Have you any idea where I put my spectacles?" asked Grandad.

page 16

round 1

1 Dad asked what sort of pizzas they would like.

2 Jane replied that she would like cheese and tomato.

3 James exclaimed that he hated cheese and tomato.

4 Dad asked James what sort he would like.

5 James decided that he would like ham and pineapple.

round 2

1 "There are no pizzas in the freezer," said Dad.

2 "What will you have instead?" asked Dad.

3 "I'll have pasta," decided Jane.

4 "I want to buy some fish and chips," said James.

5 "I think it would be a good idea to have salad," said Dad.

page 17

round 1

Is the bus late?

This ice cream tastes horrible!

That tree is going to fall!

What is that?

If you do that I will be really angry!

round 2

questions	exclamations	
request	roar	
beg	yell	
enquire	shout	
plead	cheer	
ask	cry	
implore	demand	
wonder	scream	sob

page 18

1 wouldn't

2 Tom's cat

3 "My name is Mina,"she said.

4 !

5 I can't do that.

6 I'm

7 John said that he was going to be late.

8 ?

9 the men's boat

10 must not

11 the family's car

12 "I am cold," said the old lady.

13 did not

14 he can't

15 the children's toys

16 they'll

17 Sam asked if the letter was for him.

18 they have

19 she'd

20 the babies' rattles

Grammar Section

Page 19

round 1

I mend   we mended   you will mend

we look   he looked   she will look

you paint   I painted   we shall paint

he cleans   they cleaned   I shall clean

it likes   you liked   they will like

round 2

1 Tomorrow I shall go to the library.

2 Yesterday they washed the car.

3 We shall eat the picnic later.

4 You jumped over that wall before.

5 It rained everyday last week.

page 20

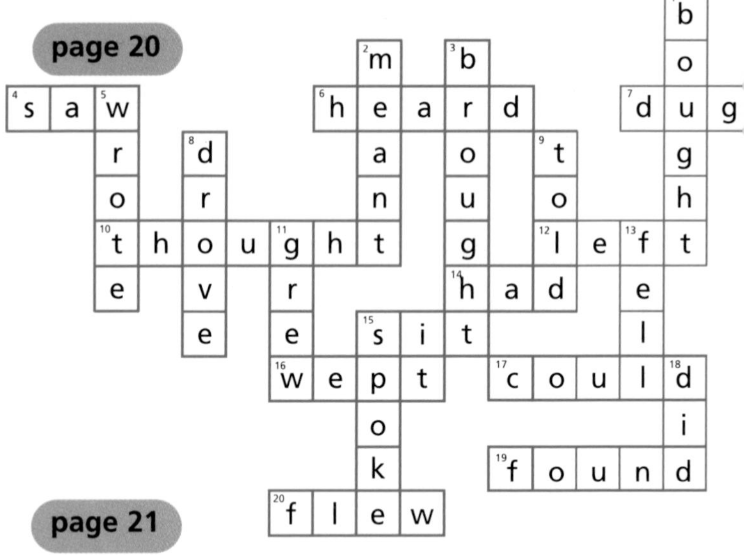

page 21

round 1

1 you were looking

2 I was laughing

3 it was barking

4 we were talking

5 they were clapping

round 2

1 they are digging

2 you are crying

3 it is raining

4 she is singing

5 I am writing

page 22

round 1	round 2
delicious	unhappy downcast depressed
fierce	tiny slight miniature
exciting	burning boiling firey
interesting	lovely attractive fair

page 23

round 1

1 I will go to the shops later. — when

2 The train screeched noisily to a halt. — how

3 It will rain today. — when

4 Have you looked everywhere? — where

5 The dog growled angrily. — how

round 2

skilfully harshly truly

frantically fully

page 24

u	r	b	e	c	a	u	s	e	l	v	a	w	l	o
n	a	g	o	a	l	u	o	v	d	u	g	w	e	x
l	y	w	f	l	t	c	u	k	a	i	z	h	q	n
e	t	n	p	i	h	s	c	d	a	f	t	e	r	h
s	r	b	d	w	o	t	u	b	v	p	m	n	l	q
s	o	f	h	c	u	k	s	i	l	f	h	y	f	l
a	z	e	m	j	g	x	a	r	b	l	x	r	j	p
q	e	q	o	t	h	e	n	c	w	b	u	t	s	n
d	f	o	l	k	x	g	d	j	w	k	m	o	z	v
e	z	r	b	y	s	y	p	t	n	h	t	j	u	m

page 25

1 I shall sing

2 they left

3 I am diving

4 old

5 how

6 and / so / because / after / before / when / although

7 he laughs

8 You were running.

9 We were laughing.

10 where

11 we skipped

12 clumsily

13 but / although / when / if

14 beautiful

15 you wrote

16 truthfully

17 It is raining.

18 when

19 so / and / when

20 it blew

Vocabulary Section

page 26

round 1

careful and attentive

toss and throw

join and connect

seldom and rarely

thrilling and exciting

round 2

1 impolite

2 rescue

3 expand

4 system

5 hidden

6 gentle

7 rare

8 normal

9 region

10 sufficient

page 27

g	i	g	a	n	t	i	c
r	h	l	u	v	o	f	g
s	u	b	k	j	u	w	r
g	g	l	a	r	g	e	e
k	e	r	a	k	j	x	a
m	a	s	s	i	v	e	t

t	n	r	o	p	j	r	t
r	e	p	l	y	t	o	e
r	k	a	r	n	j	a	l
w	h	i	s	p	e	r	l
m	f	a	q	p	l	g	r
e	m	e	n	t	i	o	n

g	m	d	a	s	h	i	p
e	b	l	g	c	o	l	j
r	q	m	h	u	r	r	y
a	p	f	c	r	o	u	l
c	r	x	j	r	v	s	e
e	g	q	f	y	v	h	k

page 28

round 1

partner rival faulty perfect settle wander

seldom often smooth rough

round 2

dis: disappear / disrespect / dishonour / disapprove/ disagree

un: unlucky / unselfish / unkind / unusual / untrue /

page 29

head + light (headlight)
rain + coat (raincoat)
foot + ball (football)
foot + man (footman)
snow + man (snowman)
snow + ball (snowball)
butter + cup (buttercup)
stair + case (staircase)
fire + fly (firefly)
fire + man (fireman)
fire + ball (fireball)
bed + jacket (bedjacket)
book + shelf (bookshelf)
book + case (bookcase)
sun + flower (sunflower)

page 30

round 1

happy: unhappy / happiness / happily

wise: wisdom / unwise

round 2

1 luckily / luckless / unlucky / unluckily
2 using / used / useful / useless
3 timing / timed / timely / untimely / timeless
4 sounding / sounded / soundly / resound
5 kindness / kindly / unkind / kindliness / unkindly

page 31

1 sick
2 eg massive / huge / gigantic
3 seldom / rarely
4 eg nightmare / nightfall / nightdress/ nightcap
5 trust
6 guard
7 unwise
8 duty
9 eg snowball / snowboard / snowbound / snowdrop
10 certain
11 eg miserable / dejected / unhappy
12 escape
13 eg hedgehog / hedgerow
14 cry
15 eg snowman / watchman / postman
16 unworthy
17 eg attractive / beautiful
18 disallow
19 eg firefly / butterfly
20 eg remarked / noted / cried / yelled / whispered

page 32

1 "**It's** already five o'clock!" moaned Ali.
3 The dog made a tremendous noise and **its** barking woke me up.
4 I like the cherry tree with **its** beautiful blossom.
6 **It's** very unusual to get snow in summer.
8 I am really excited because **it's** my birthday tomorrow!
9 The football is lost so **it's** the end of the game.
10 The sandcastle lost **its** walls when the wave came.

page 33

1 I know **whose** coat that is.
2 The boy **who's** riding the new bike is my friend.
4 "**Who's** got the tickets?" asked dad.

5 **"Who's** going to make a cup of tea?" asked Mum.

1 **There** are thirty days in September.

3 "I'm sure **there** is a quicker way," said Paul.

4 **Their** bags were very heavy.

5 They put up **their** hands when they knew the answer.

page 34

1 What **were** you doing yesterday?

3 Although they **were** cold, they wanted to finish building the snowman.

4 **Where** is the cricket bat?

5 **"**I'm sure your book will be **where** you left it," said the teacher.

1 "I **know** what I'm doing!" snapped John.

3 There are **no** clouds in the sky today.

4 "Do you **know** the time?" asked the old lady.

5 There is **no** reason to be frightened.

page 35

1 "**Your** work is very good," said the teacher.

2 You can find **your** way by using the map.

3 If **you're** not well you should stay in bed.

4 I really enjoyed **your** birthday party.

2 It will be **too** late to go soon.

3 Only **two** days until our holidays!

4 The dog wanted **to** chase the cat.

5 If we want **to** catch the train, we must leave now.

page 36

The words in **bold** and the orange patches show the corrections.

Passage 1

There was going to be a **fair** at the edge of town. Sam and Tom were **hoping** to go in the morning.

"How long can we stay for?" asked Tom.

"About an **hour**," said Mum.

"I **haven't** got any money,**"** moaned Sam.

"I will give you some," said Mum, **"**but you mustn't spend it all on sweets."

The **boys were** very excited and they couldn't **wait** until it was time **to** go.

When they woke up the next morning, the sun was **shining**.

They got out of bed and **ate** a good breakfast before they set off. They **were** very careful crossing the road and they arrived just as the gates were opening.

Passage 2

I remember my first day in school. It was when I **was** five years old. My teacher was called Mrs Lowry. Although I was very little, I **felt** very grown up as I **walked** into the **classroom**.

I was **sitting** in the front next to a boy called Paul. We spent the first half of the morning **writing** the letters of the alphabet. We had fifteen minutes for playtime and we **were** given a drink of milk and a **biscuit**.

After playtime Mrs Lowry read us a story about a family of **foxes** and a **hare** with very long ears. We then had to draw a picture but I **couldn't** draw the fox very well. **Paul's** picture was great. He said that he liked to draw.

page 37

Passage 3

Mrs Horner wanted to buy some fruit. She went into the little shop and **spoke** to Mr Long.

"Good morning**,** Mr Long,**"** she said. "I hope **you've** some fresh fruit today."

"Of course, Mrs Horner. My fruit is **always** fresh."

"**I'd** like some apples and **pears**," she said.' 'Those **strawberries** look good. I **bought** some of those last week and they **were** delicious."

"**It's** the **right** time of the year for them," remarked Mr Long. "How **many** apples would you like?"

"Six please," replied Mrs Horner. "**I'll** take some bananas, **too**. I **am** very fond of banana sandwiches."

Passage 4

Not a sound could be **heard** in the wood. **There** was a covering of snow on the ground and the **leaves** on the trees **were** white.

Suddenly, the snow **began** to fall again from the heavy, grey clouds. A small badger scurried through the trees on **its** way home. It **stopped** by a large oak tree and sniffed the air. It sensed danger! **Where** was it **coming** from**?** The badger **didn't** wait **to** find out. It **ran** quickly into the nearby **bushes** and made **no** movement until the danger had passed.

page 38

1 ripping
2 knives
3 "Are you hurt?" cried the boy.
4 peaceable
5 h
6 !
7 necessary
8 Who's
9 witch
10 wrapped
11 gentle
12 the dog's bone
13 unusual
14 he looks
15 polite
16 I've
17 their
18 I was riding
19 The ladies' hats were very colourful.
20 Billy asked if he could go now.

page 39

1 I slept
2 b
3 the children's toys
4 courageous
5 amusing
6 feet
7 disagree
8 won't
9 manage
10 flipped
11 The zoo keeper shouted that the lion had escaped.
12 Where
13 pale
14 eg knee / know / knew / knowledge / knuckle / knife etc
15 "Look out!" shouted the policeman.
16 The ox's cart was heavy.
17 waving
18 ?
19 were
20 although

page 40

1 the babies' coats
2 rough
3 You're
4 you were playing
5 batter
6 exciting
7 "That was very funny!" laughed Sulim.
8 interest
9 echoes
10 its
11 aloud
12 was
13 e
14 The children's poems are very good.
15 noticeable
16 too
17 liked
18 Linda said that it was the best film she had ever seen.
19 we'll
20 because